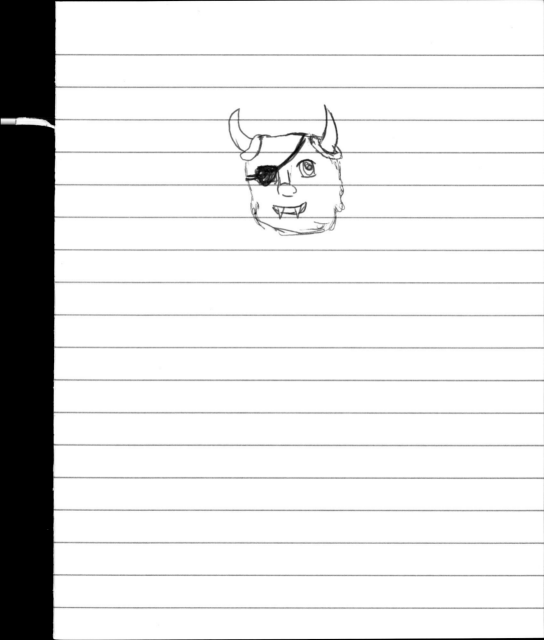

- 21/12/19

liz mas
xoxo

Will you stop eating! **Lizz**
Your bestfriend is missing

I can see them too
your just as sane as i am

he's covered in blood again
Why is it he's always covered in blood
everything
Don't worry harry we'll explain when
we get back to headquaters

Don't call me Nymphadora

22/12/19

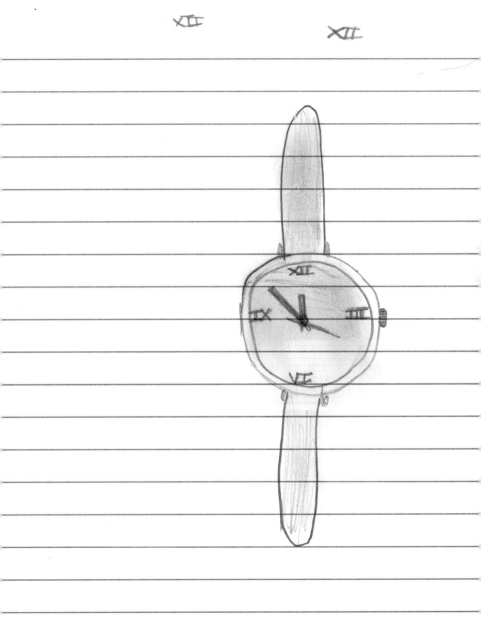

love potion ∞

ooga booga

ya yeet

.